NOT TONIGHT

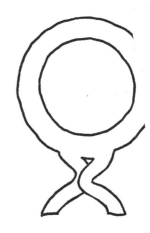

Riana Duncan

 Robson Books

For Andrew Fraser

First published in Great Britain in 1987 by Robson Books Ltd,
Bolsover House, 5–6 Clipstone Street, London W1P 7EB.

Copyright 1986 Riana Duncan

British Library Cataloguing in Publication Data

Duncan, Riana
  Not tonight!
  1. English wit and humour, Pictorial
  I. Title
  741.5942   NC1479

ISBN 0–86051–458–7

Printed in Great Britain by
St Edmundsbury Press Ltd, Bury St Edmunds, Suffolk

THE KAMA SUTRA of ancient Indian literature has long been regarded as the pinnacle of erotic refinement, yet its British counterpart, although less flamboyant, can be no less valid for that.

Cultural and climatic differences have played their role in determining a low-key and possibly more prosaic approach to the subject, but with its own richness of variety.

The innate modesty of the British and a natural inclination to sweep sexual matters under the bedclothes mean that the English language abounds in euphemisms for the sex act.

Some, such as how's yer father, nudge nudge wink wink, seem a little obscure if suggestive, while others reflect a dormant and deeply buried playfulness in the British character: slap and tickle, hanky panky. There are descriptive words like leg-over and nookie, and simple phrases which do no more than hint at it: making it, having it off. Perhaps the most widely used of all the euphemisms for sexual intercourse is the term sleeping with someone, an accurate enough assessment of what goes on.

In the newfound climate of linguistic liberation, with the freedom to say condom condom condom, there is a danger that these many and varied euphemistic expressions will disappear forever from the language and sex will be, simply, sex.

Meanwhile, this book is about It.

Indian texts separate the lovemaking postures into six categories.

The British defy such pigeonholing by sheer diversity.

Lying back and thinking of England is just one of many variations on a theme.

THE CONSENSUS

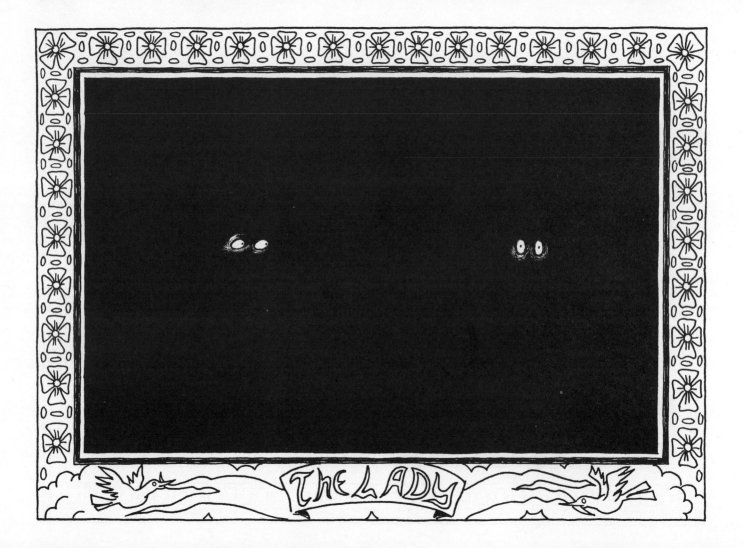

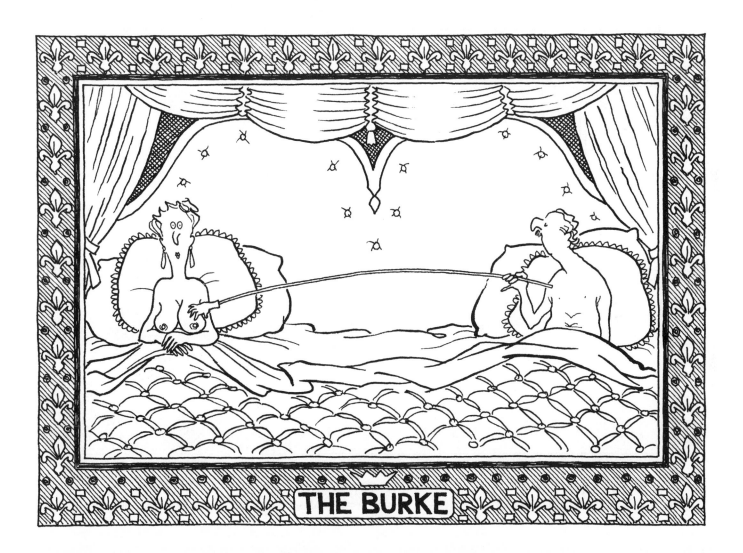

THE BURKE

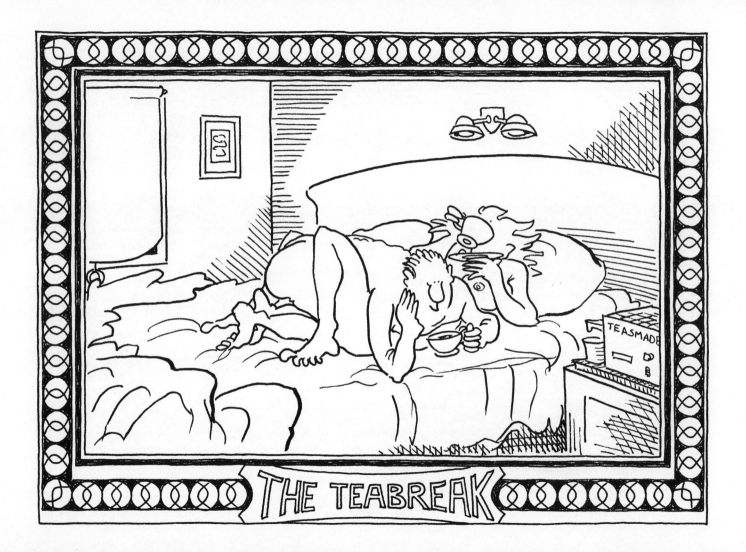

THE TEABREAK

THE CLIMAX

THE ARGUMENT

FOREPLAY is what sometimes precedes the sex act, a sort of hors d'oeuvre before the main course. As women are more slow to arousal than men, foreplay can serve as a jolly useful way of letting the woman know what's up. As it were.

Foreplay among the British is traditionally kept simple and is often limited to removing trousers and underpants (socks optional); switching off the tv; switching off the light.

THE FREEMASON

THE FUMBLER

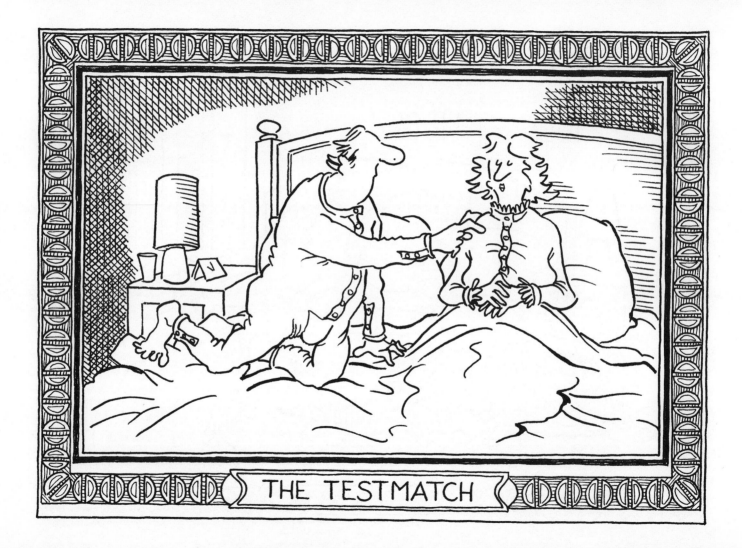

THE TESTMATCH

THE OPTIMIST

THE MISSIONARY POSITION

THE MOGADON

THE *REFUSAL*

ORGASM is what it's all about, the prize at the end of the hundred-yard sprint. As with most races, there is usually only one winner.

In fact, for some women the First could be compared to the Second Coming – seemingly impossible, but you've got to believe in it.

Orgasm is often associated with an awful lot of noise (involuntary vocalisation and poorly sprung beds). Nice people, of coure, keep quiet.

Possibly in consequence of a lousy climate and inadequately heated bedrooms, orgasmic response in the Brit is more commonly located in the nose and is then called a sneeze.

The sexual climax is sometimes said to make the earth move.

It is important to remember that earthquakes are very, very rare in Britain and when they do occur, are more in the nature of a ripple than a quake. Seismic, like sexual, activity is temperate.

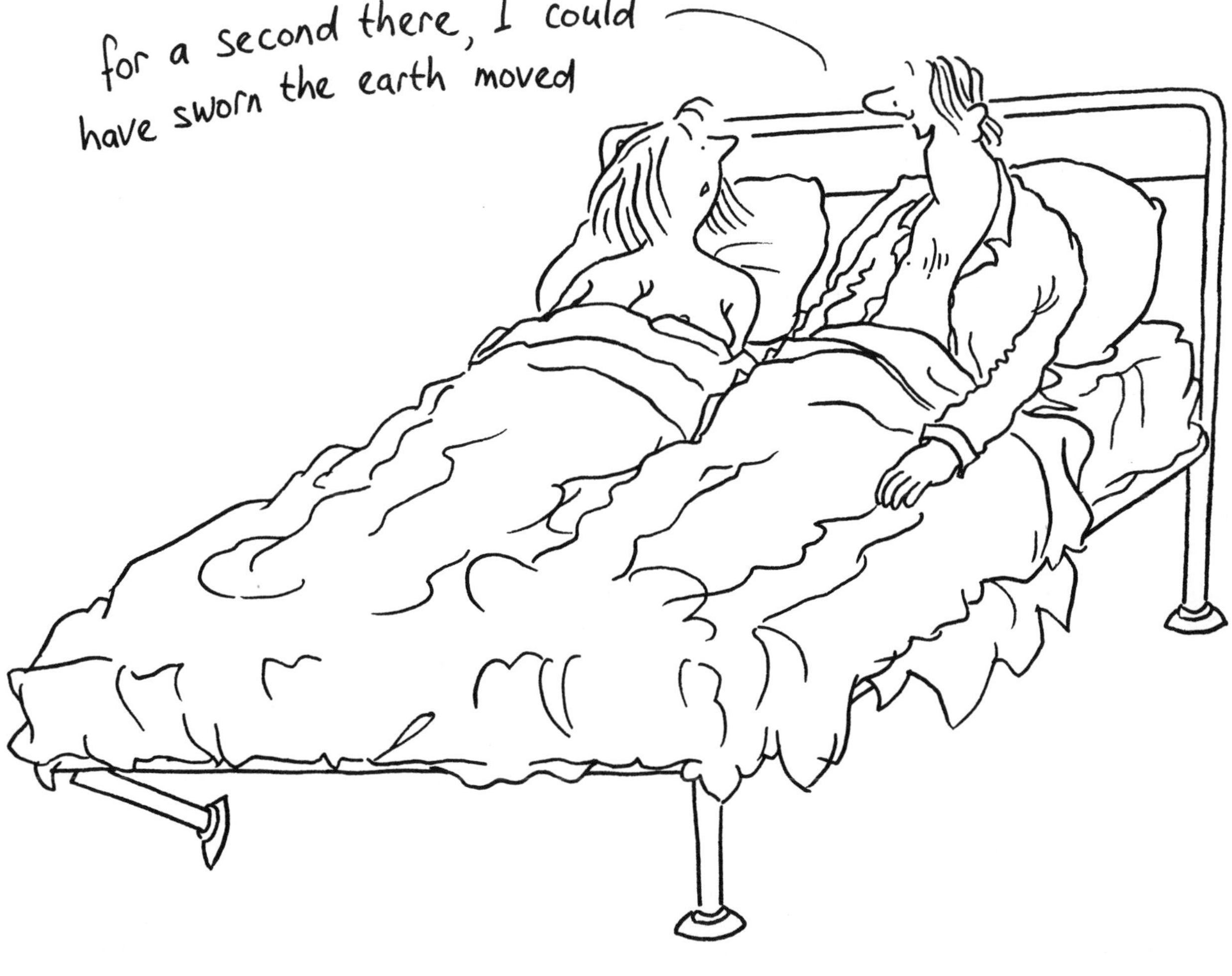
for a second there, I could have sworn the earth moved

THE COUNCIL FLAT

COITUS INTERRUPTUS

THE STATISTIC OR 2.5 TIMES A WEEK

THE *QUICKIE*

THE *COSMO* READER

THE FEMINIST

EROGENOUS ZONES are the

points and places which, when stimulated, lead to sexual passion.

In the male, the main erogenous zones are the stomach, the eye and the typing pool.

In the female, the areas which respond most strongly to erotic stimuli are centred around the palm, the wrist, the fourth finger of the left hand and the boss's sanctum.

THE HARD DAY AT THE OFFICE

WILLY NIL-LY

GRANDSTAND

THE POWER CUT

THE EDUCATED GUESS

SEARCHING FOR THE NEEDLE IN THE HAYSTACK

APHRODISIACS are sexual turn-ons and part of the problem with sex is that what turns on men doesn't necessarily turn on women, and vice versa.

The basic difference is that while a man may be stimulated by the sight of a woman in a see-through blouse, the woman will be turned on by the price tag on that see-through blouse.

In the same way that the tight skirt of Miss Winters in Accounts will have an aphrodisiacal effect on the male, a fat wallet and a healthy bank account act as powerful stimuli for the female.

Risk-taking acts as an effective stimulant on men and women both, although being cited as co-respondent tends to undo its aphrodisiac qualities.

Power is another well-known aphrodisiac and absolute power turns on absolutely.

A POTTED HISTORY OF THE TWIN
APHRODISIACS POWER AND DANGER

Women are turned on by drink. Men think they are.

THE LARGE SWEET SHERRY

THE NIGHT OUT WITH THE LADS

THE BEERDRINKER

THE CRUX

THE **MIDLIFE** CRISIS

CONSENTING ADULTS

THE DIFFERENCE

PHALLIC SYMBOLS serve,

among other things, as indicators of a society's attitude to sex and its rating within that culture.

As a basic rule of thumb, a thing can be called a phallic symbol if it's longer than it's wide; a thumb is therefore arguably phallic, although it has to be said its role is more often that of a substitute than a symbol.

Age-old rituals and traditions, their meaning lost in time, have survived to give us that most enduring of Anglo-Saxon phallic symbols, the rolling pin.

Looking at the general shape and proportions of guns and fishing tackle, it is easy to see the British fondness for shootin' and fishin' as an expression of suppressed sexual desires.

Most ball games are phallic. Cricket, in fact, typifies the British way of sex: long periods of lying around doing nothing and incomprehensible to foreigners when it comes to scoring.

Cars are widely held to be phallic symbols. This explains, possibly, the phenomenal success in Britain of the Mini.

Seemingly staid, the traditional City Gent, with his rolled-up umbrella, his rolled-up *Financial Times,* and his pinstripe suit, is actually making a very personal statement about himself.

THE PRIORITY

THE BRAGGART

THE SUBSTITUTE

THE DARTBOARD

AFTERPLAY is a misnomer. It implies, at the very least, the involvement of two people. Playing with oneself is a different matter altogether and comes, so to speak, under deviation.

From the male point of view the act of love can be divided into three stages of rolling on, off and over; the final stage is often associated with the type of involuntary vocalisation known as snoring. This tends to leave the female, who may just have woken up to what is going on, in a state of limbo, which in this context can be interpreted as arousal.

In Britain, afterplay is often replaced by a hot drink and a cold bath.

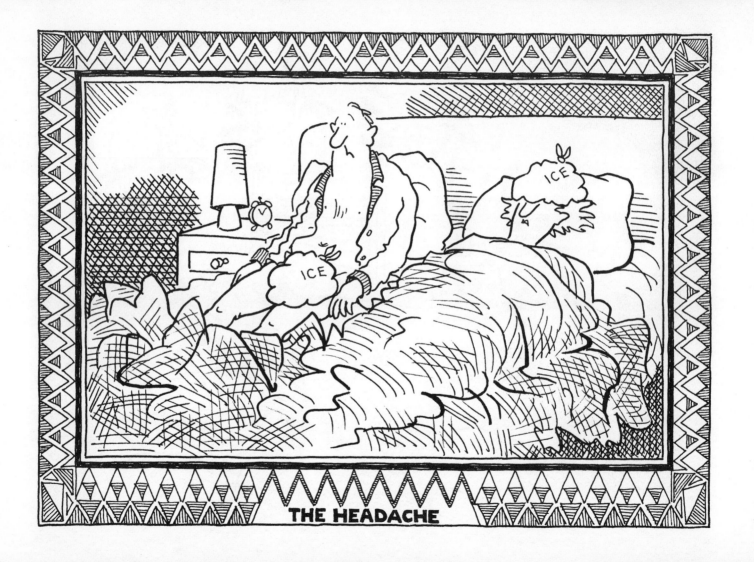

THE HEADACHE

THE CLIMATE

THE GREAT DIVIDE

STALEMATE

THE GREAT UNWASHED

PIG IN A POKE

CONCEPTION is frequently the result of believing the other to be looking after contraception.

Fertility seems to peak just when the bank manager has turned down your overdraft, when the wife has picked up a rumour of extra-curricular activities, or after that one little drink more, no I really mustn't, go on twist my arm, oh well what the hell.

The classic male response to the classic female condition is a very good question indeed.

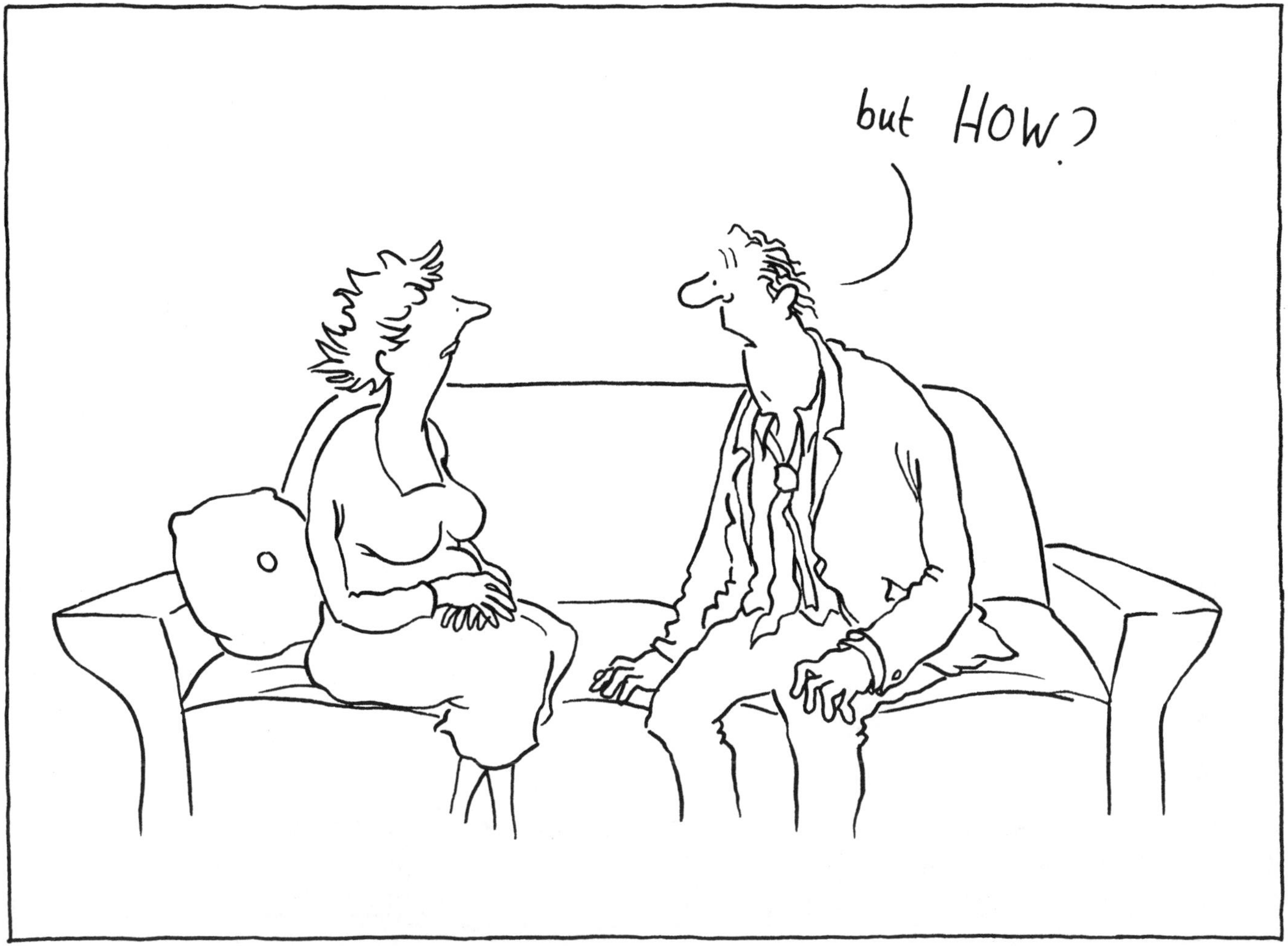
but HOW?

THE ENIGMA VARIATION

THE FOOTBALL KNEE

THE PAIN IN THE NECK

TRUE BRIT

THE EXECUTIVE

THE WORKAHOLIC

DEVIATION is a departure from the norm. An open, frank and spontaneous approach to sex would therefore undoubtedly qualify as deviation.

To give another example: when a woman dresses in men's clothes, it is fashion; when a man dresses in women's clothing, that is deviation. Exempt from this are those males whose profession involves the wearing of gowns. This is merely a peculiarity of the country's institutions and is not usually thought of as deviation, except when accessories are worn.

THE NORM   DEVIATION FROM THE NORM

One of the more common forms of deviation is exhibitionism, the exposure of genitals to an unwilling viewer. This, by
definition, rules out women. All flashers are male. Q.E.D.

EXHIBITIONISM

NARCISSISM

VENTILATION

When a person, for the sake of argument to be referred to as an adult, applies a cane to, roughly speaking, the genital area of another person who is under age, it is not deviation but an aspect of the British public school system and, as such, character-building. Flogging can be called deviation only if the practice continues after A-levels.

AN ENGLISHMAN'S PYJAMAS ARE HIS BONDAGE

THE UNSPEAKABLE

96

THE TUNNEL OF LOVE

THE CIVIL SERVANT

POSITIONS developed for maximum practicality of purpose and minimum waste of energy, in keeping with the British scale of priorities.

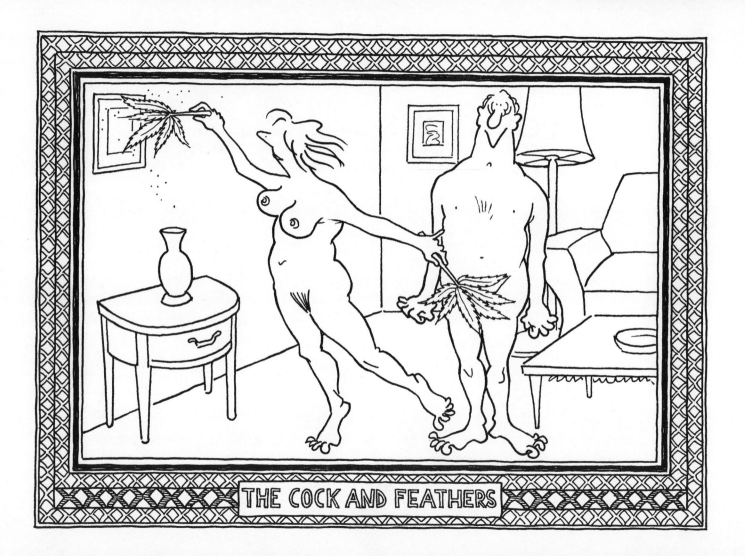

THE COCK AND FEATHERS

KNITTING A SWEATER

DOING THE DISHES

FIXING SUPPER

THE WINCHESTER BYPASS

SEX may be what makes the rest of the world go round, we in Britain know that there is a time and a place for everything and sex isn't everything. Like mountains, it is there, that's all — a natural enough attitude in a nation with a talent for restraint and an inclination, given the choice, to place a higher value on a nice cup of tea. Anything else wouldn't be cricket.

From the British perspective, sex is all right . . .

but it will never replace the bicycle.